SELF-MADE IN THE DARK

SAMUEL B PROFIT III

Published by Published by Owner of Inside My Mind Publishing LLC.
Andrea T. Robinson

Self-Made In The Dark

ISBN: 9798643006558

Unless otherwise noted, all scriptures are derived from the English Standard Version of the Bible and from the Qur'an.

Book Cover Deign by goonwrite.com

Printed in the United States of America

DEDICATION

I want to dedicate this book to a person that I am the most thankful for: *Me*! The old me! Thank you for choosing the path that you chose to travel, which landed us where we are today. You were nowhere near perfect, but you always felt the need to make the best decision possible, even though we were in the belly of the beast (prison). Thank you for wanting better for yourself, and me.

Sincerely, "The future you".

CONTENTS

Introduction "A Letter To The Youth"   i

Thank You For The Truth   iii

1	Self-Made In The Dark	5
2	The Reason	7
3	The Reason for 270 Steps	9
4	The Reason For Love	10
5	The Reason I Still Remember	13
6	The Reason You Don't Trust Me	15
7	The Reason For Shannon Elijah	17
8	The Reason I Call You Grandma	18
9	Leah Inspired Me	19
10	Who Am I	20
11	Get To Know Me	23
12	Scattered Thoughts: "Do You"	35
13	Tenacity	37
14	Unbroken	40
15	I Met 3 Men	42
16	Dear Love	44
17	To My Ancestors	46

18   To My People "The Original People"   48

19   Imagine This   50

20   Mind Not Incarcerated   52

21   It's Not Easy   53

22   Dreaming: "The Sun"   54

23   Poems Of An Underdog   60-

- Me and You
- Family & Friends
- She's Gone
- In Love Alone
- Forgive Me
- Mental Strength
- What My Life's Like
- Wake Up
- Happy Anniversary
- Necessary Behavior
- What Eye See
- Real Don't Exist
- I Stand Alone
- Responsibility
- Dear Momma
- Power U
- A True Women
- The Perfect Day
- Dog Tags
- Take Care Of Business
- Ms. Anonymous
- Just Speaking The Truth
- My Look Is Original
- Without You
- R.I.P
- She Came & Left On Her Birthday

- Rest and Live In Peace Y'all
- Quotes That Inspired Me
- The Difference Between a Boy and a Man

Introduction

"A LETTER TO THE YOUTH"

Dear Youth,

Enjoy the time you have as a child, because you're only young once. Try your best to keep the advice and wisdom given to you by your elders. Some wisdom I'll give you to think about is. "While young and strong, prepare for the time you're old and weak". This piece of wisdom may be difficult for you to understand right now or, you just may not care at this time, which is okay because every seed that is planted needs time to grow. Experience is the best teacher. the sad thing is that "it only takes one mistake" to end all you ever knew. My wish for you is to be attracted to great influences, and to make decisions that are "only" beneficial. nobody is perfect, but please don't ever use this saying as an excuse to justify simple minded things. After answering this question, imagine your current self-having a conversation with the future you as a 30-year-old adult. When you see this person (your favorite self) you're probably hoping they'll have a smile on their face with kisses and hugs for you, and thanking you, But reality tells no lies, and great isn't always the outcome of the future. If the future, you have tears in their eyes and really isn't too happy for you. Your past decisions probably weren't good ones. The truth of the matter is that you are in control, and whatever you strive for is what you're going to end up with. Whether you end up with something or you end up with nothing; It's what you strived for. Question: If life is what you make it, what are you shaping?

Thank You For The Truth

To my family, who never made time for me when I was actually at the lowest point in my life, you told people not to give me your phone number and your heart smiled at the pain I suffered. Thank you for showing me the real you. To my friends, who I put myself in harmful situations for with no questions asked. Where were you? I didn't need an organ (heart, kidney, lung, etc...). I only needed a little support emotionally. I would have given my life for you; you wouldn't lend me a hand. Thank you for showing me what I really mean to you. To the women I was intimate with, you moved on to the next man pretty quick. You probably didn't think I'd have bright future after prison. Just remember that when I told you I love you, I meant it. To you all, I accept you for who you are, and I promise you two things: (1) I'm not mad at you, and (2) our bond will never be the way it was in the past. Thank you for the truth! The betrayal demonstrated by you really hurt me, and I live with it day in and day out- year after year. *Thank you for the truth!*

CHAPTER 1

SELF-MADE IN THE DARK

In the dark I sat for a while; my whole world was pitch black but there was a generator plugged into the energy that my soul possesses. The secret to life reveals itself in the dark where no man can see (this is how all things are born). for us all, there are two choices when times are difficult... Be born or miss the opportunity to exist. I chose to grab at the pieces of me that tried quickly to flee. In that very moment it was time to start pulling myself together and start shaping. What did I shape? He who is unbreakable. The more I shaped, the brighter the light shined.

Love ones counted me out faster than those that hated me, but the universe makes no mistakes. The less I have to lean or depend on, the stronger I will be, in which I'm hated because I'm so strong. As an infant I was delivered into the world and had no choice but to live as my teachers (parents) understood. Now I see through the eyes of a warrior and hold on with all my might to my own understanding. understanding that the world is flooded with conflict and I have to be aggressive and energetic when attacking all obstacles that present themselves. Self-Made In The Dark; I was the light the entire time.

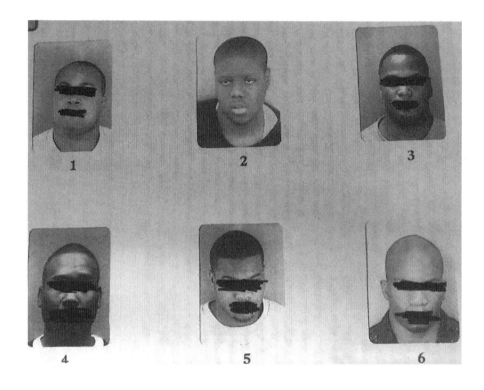

CHAPTER 2

THE REASON

TO: Kiesha, Tamara, Dominique, Shawn, Mercedes, Shannon, Nardo, and Darnell. This letter is to you, my biological siblings. I really would like to sit down with you to have a much-needed conversation. My current situation won't allow it, so I'll try my best to make my words felt, and I hope you receive them. I'm the eldest of us all, so therefore I'm responsible for us all no matter if I want to be or not. To my sisters that I love so much, you're perfect in the eyes of your big brother and that'll never change even if you woke up one day and decided to hate me. To my warriors, my little brothers, I love you guys all the same and there's not a single thing that I won't go through with you. As I sit here and write these words to you my eyes are filled with water because I sat back and reflected on the bond we had growing up. There really wasn't one and sometimes I feel like a bond will never be. These are just my feelings. Unfortunately, we didn't grow up together as O'Neill's in the same household, which means we were divided. In being divided we were groomed by two different families that never came together for greater good of the children. Not to mention being raised by two different parents that had a non-family spouse to please, but our parents did have one thing in common. "A child". The children were being pulled in two different

7

directions mentally. To make a long story short, everyone was on a different page. With everyone on different pages how can we be a healthy functioning union. The beauty of it all is that we still love each other, and individually we're not damaged. Thanks to the strength engraved into our DNA. When I was young and crazy, prison would never be a part of my future (in my mind), and I actually thought I had all the time in the world to get my life on track and fix all that I fucked up. Not to mention the vices that held me hostage along with my lower self that I favored over my higher self. It's only my fault. I'll never blame a single person for my issues. Since I've been incarcerated, the only time I smile about living life is when I imagine myself living it under different conditions. During my incarceration I reached out to each and every one of you, but not everyone reached back out to me. Maybe the timing wasn't right; whatever the reason, I love you anyway. Before ending these words, I can't leave out the women that brought us all into this world. I want to thank you for allowing life to happen to the individuals I'm most dedicated to and will lay down my life for. Without you being the bridge between our father and life itself, we would not exist. The reason for this great distance is due to my decisions, please forgive me and be confident that I'll never let you down again.

CHAPTER 3

THE REASON FOR 270 STEPS

The first step I took I fell into dark waters, 29 steps after that I stopped stepping, and I started swimming. 30 steps after that I found a sleeping bag with oxygen in it. 30 steps after that I meditated. 30 steps after that something started to form around my mind. 30 steps after that I noticed that my sleeping bag had expanded. 30 steps after that I started to try and stretch myself out. 30 steps after that I began hearing familiar voices in my head, but I didn't know where they were coming from. 30 steps after that I started to have visions of a woman who couldn't wait to meet me. 30 steps after that my meditation came to an end, and it was time to reveal the new me. Each step represents a day, 270 days = 9 months. At the end of this cycle, life introduces to the world a new he or she. During different times we all traveled the same path. We were equipped with intelligence before we learned of our existence, so if you made all 270 steps before you had legs, you should never downplay your greatness.

CHAPTER 4

THE REASON FOR LOVE

Love is one of the many ingredients existing within us since the beginning of creation. Love is the highest form of understanding. Water is life, right? The reason I asked is because without blood flowing through every organ delivering oxygen, and other properties needed to keep us healthy, we'd be in trouble. Our blood is water and minerals. The body is 75% water, containing life sustaining properties. Our brains sit's on water, if not properly hydrated then the body will not work properly. So, I feel that understanding the beauty of ourselves, and the intelligence within ourselves is also understanding the love given from the universe, creator, or whatever you call your higher power. When a man has a family, he should understand his duty and responsibility as a provider, protector, and a teacher. When he honestly does right by his wife in and outside of her presence, it's not because he's perfect, but he loves his family as he should.

In the Bible, *I Corinthians 13:4-8* talks about love it says:

Love is patient and kind; love does not envy or boast; it is not arrogant or rude. It does not insist on its own way; it is not irritable or resentful; it does not rejoice at wrongdoing but rejoices with the truth. Love bears all things, believes all things, hopes all things, endures all things. Love never ends. As for prophecies, they will pass way; as for tongues, they will cease; as for knowledge, it will pass away.

Love is something that is great.

These scriptures were shared with me by a good friend assuring me she'll remain in my corner through the toughest of times. The love she has for me is heavenly love.

An elder gentleman I used to have green tea and bagels with every Saturday morning, loved my perception of things, and I loved his perception of life. I was so good at making money cutting hair and selling edibles that I made in the microwave. The old guy asked me.

"Where do you see yourself in seven years after your release from prison? Ish Allah!" (He's Muslim, and Ish Allah means God willing).

I responded, "With the plans and projects, I have written down in my book of life, seven years off the prison yard I should be worth $10 million or more to be sure that not only mine, but my family's future is secure as well".

Later that day, he said he wanted me to read something from the Qur'an, Surah 28: 76-77 read:

Indeed, Qur'an was from the people of Moses, but he tyrannized them. And we gave him of treasures whose keys would burden a band of strong men; thereupon his people said to him, "Do not exult. Indeed, Allah does not like that exultant. But seek, through that which Allah has given you, the home of the hereafter; and [yet], do not forget your share of the world. And do good as Allah has done good to you. And desire not corruption in the land.

Indeed, Allah does not like corrupters".

After reading this passage, I took it as my brother reminding me to always remain humble and help others. The love he demonstrated was brotherly love, and I thanked him. No matter who a person may be or their personal views, ethnic background, tax bracket, or attitude. I want the best for all of us, the flesh of a man will not allow he/she to love anyone, (relative or stranger) unconditionally. Love like that can only be shown through people from the Divine. The reason for Love is because the world would already be on fire without it.

CHAPTER 5

THE REASON I STILL REMEMBER IS BECAUSE IT STILL HURTS

I still remember sitting on the porch with my younger brother Shawn; both of us bored on a nice summer day. Enjoying the weather, watching females, cars, and kids laughing and playing, passing by our house. I rarely spent time with my little brothers, so I said,

"Let's go to the park and play a few games of basketball."

The look on Shawn's face was like I just said what he'd been wanting me to say forever. He jumped up with excitement.

"Sam, is you really for real?" He asked me with the biggest smile on his face.

"Yes, I'm for real lil bro" I replied.

He went in the house to change into full basketball gear along with his brand-new basketball. Walking down the street towards the park he smiled about how bad he's going to beat me. Of course, I participated with my share of trash talk as well. Minutes before we were able to make it to the park, a car turned the corner, drove up to the curb with the driver yelling out of the window.

"What up?"

It was my best friend Curtis.

"Come on and ride with me bro, I got some females waiting on us." He yelled!

Before I could even think about the words needed to cancel the time I was supposed to spend with my brother, we locked eyes for no longer than a couple seconds. He saw it coming and without speaking a word, Shawn turned and walked away from me with tears in his eyes. I told him that I'll make it up to him, but he ignored me. I haven't seen my brother since that day, which was 13 years to this writing. Shawn, I'm sorry, please forgive me and believe me when I say that our relationship means the world to me and I love you with everything in me lil brother. Even if you hate me deep down in your heart, you have every right to, but it'll do nothing more than strengthen my love for you. The reason I still remember is because it still hurts.

CHAPTER 6

THE REASON YOU DON'T TRUST ME

To My Mother, the reason you don't trust me is because I've never given you a reason to, I showed you that you can't, and I always seem to make bad decisions. The fact that I'm so damn secretive doesn't make it any better. For as long as I was old enough to leave home to play in the streets or around the neighborhood, our relationship was me being a recipient of your anger. I felt that all I had was myself, and any female who filled the void of me being unable to talk to you about my problems. The older I got, the more of a problem I was becoming. I'm the reason you were terminated from section 8 housing, making life a bit more difficult for you, and I apologize for that. I wasn't even around to struggle with you and my brothers. Unfortunately, I went to prison shortly after the termination was finalized from assisted housing. All that I put you through while I was growing up is unbelievable, but yet you still manage to tell me you love me at the end of every phone call. I brought guns and drugs into your home, and often downplayed the dangers that came with the lifestyle I lived. My little brothers looked up to me, but I failed to be attentive and a positive example of what a man is. As I sit and reflect on the past, I probably wouldn't have trusted me either. As I stand here today in a mirror, I'm 32 years old with enough ingredients to fill five men with great substance, and soon I'll be able to see you smile happily with an unforced smiled and tears of joy in your pretty eyes. The day is near that you will say to me *I trust you!*

CHAPTER 7

THE REASON FOR SHANNON ELIJAH

Y ou were brought into this world to show us what real love is and what it should look like. All you've ever been was yourself, showing everyone whose been blessed with the opportunity to have been in your presence that love can be felt by something as simple as a smile. So innocent is my baby brother, the only person I know that will never have an enemy. You're my favorite person Shannon. While your two elder brothers made poor choices in life leaving our mom behind for years at a time, you stayed by her side day in and day out. Yeah lil brother, I look up to you with eyes that only see you as a precious gift. Shannon Elijah. What a powerful name that only you can hold. I'm honored to be your big brother, Momma's greatest son; We love you.

CHAPTER 8

THE REASON I CALL YOU GRANDMA

Dominque (My Twin), I call you grandma, but I'm not pushing a joke at you. You earned that name because of your moral's little sis. I'm proud of the woman you've grown into after going through all that you did growing up. You possessed strength before you knew you were strong, so stop questioning yourself, pick a direction and go. You and your children (my brilliant nieces and nephews) presence in my life means the world to me. Being incarcerated isn't easy but after conversation and a few laughs with my little partners (DeAnnah, Ua'Niah, Demyah, Jr., Braylon, and Omarion), I feel like I was free for a day. I want nothing short of the best for you, because you deserve it. Thank you for loving me unconditionally when I needed you the most. I have no idea where that love grew from, but you're definitely appreciated, and I love you for that Grandma. You're such a Blessing. I'm working hard to be home before you become a wife to a lucky man, so that I can witness my little sister take the walk that'll be the first step into the next chapter of her life. I Love you.

CHAPTER 9

LEAH INSPIRED ME

Hi Leah, My one of a kind niece. I love you and your brother so much. I've always wondered to myself if you think about me from time to time. Every time I ask your mom how you're doing, she tells me how you have so much attitude, personality, and confidence. I love to hear that about you, it puts a smile on my face every time because she's totally clueless as to where "how you act" comes from, but I'm not. See Leah, as you know, you were born prematurely so you had to fight for your life. You made it and I'm so thankful for you. You had to be a fighter to survive. During the times you come off as cocky or over confident, it's just you're still releasing the energy that's been present since the beginning that helped you win your fight against the energy that tried to end your existence. while you fought for your life, I was going through a situation also and I wasn't sure how to make it through. when I received the news that you pulled through, I was inspired to fight through my situation as well. No matter how long it may take, or who's standing by my side and who's not. You're my Blessing Leah, I'm amazed at how you demonstrated strength before you knew you were strong. I love you little one, you're my inspiration.

CHAPTER 10

WHO AM I

I'm the guy struggling to purify his perception of life. I am a man that wasn't educated about who I really am. My ancestor's tribe. Our real name; Or the way of their culture. Many people have said to me "a woman can't raise a man", but I'm proud to say that I was raised by a woman. The Bible shows that Adam & Eve were born Ethiopia (Babylon), so Ethiopia is my home. My skin resembles the hue that brought everything into existence. I am a man who handpicked all the ingredients needed to grow a new me. I am he who's hated for being a reflection of those existing from the beginning; original. I appreciate the simple things that life has to offer because to me, simple is priceless. I'm the father of every child that is in need, I am the strength for every woman that lacks the ability to be strong. I am the big brother to every man who lost his way. I am flesh that's temporary with an infinite mind. I'm the truth which is the light. So I have a clear vision in the dark. I am love, peace, understanding, kind, forgiving, patient, righteous, happiness, wisdom, protection, intelligence, and unity. I am also Black, Brown, Yellow, White, poverty, success, fear, courage, and if you're this, *I am you too!*

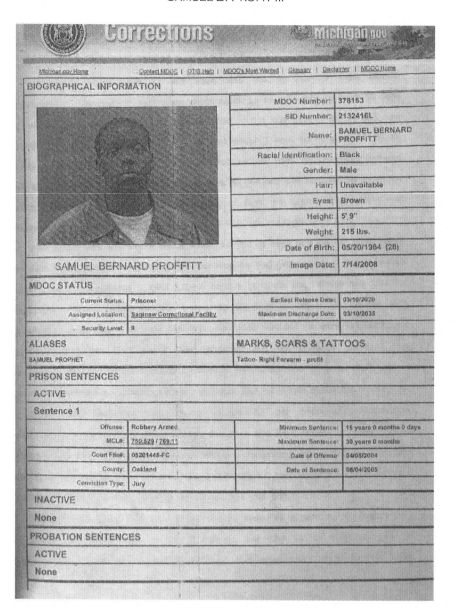

CHAPTER 11

GET TO KNOW ME

Hello world, my name is Samuel. I was introduced to the world May 20, 1984, in Detroit, Michigan. I'm thankful for my parents, Ms. Wanda Grooms and Mr. Sam Profit, fortunately they were both a part of my life. Though my mom and dad weren't together, they did a great job coparenting. Mom was a single mother of 3 boys, Shannon, Shawn, and me. She did better than great raising us, "you did a helluva job mom and we love you so much, you are the strongest woman I know". For the most part. We had it hard financially. Homes without heat during the cold winter months forcing us to use the oven to heat the house, boiled water to bathe in, and necessity to sleep together in one room. We walked miles in the snow to the nearest grocery store because we didn't have transportation at times. Money was so scarce that we were forced to relocate so many times in a two-year span that it created turbulence in my young mind. Moving around so much, I attended several elementary schools throughout my city; Nine in total. Even though there was so much instability, I still proved to be an intelligent youngster, always received great report cards and progress reports. All the struggles I was blessed with as a child made me independent, relentless, and determined. My dad on the other hand was much secured financially, in my eyes. He helped us out a great deal of times, all the while he had his own household to worry about. I wouldn't trade him for anything in this world, his presence in my life is very important to me and the wisdom and ingredients he passed down to me will last as long as our bloodline. "I love you Dad, and the bond that we have is priceless." As a child, I would always enjoy the company and stories of my elders. Listening to all that wisdom did something to my soul that was unexplainable. My great grandmother Mary told me the best stories because she was the eldest person in my family, so she took me back further than anyone else could and she painted a vivid picture in my mind every time. Her mother, my great-great grandmother, was a slave. A very beautiful woman with a beautiful name to match her features and personality. Genesis; Grandmother Mary would tell me how Grandma Genesis took her to cotton fields with her sometimes. Her mom told jokes and stories that helped mask her reality and little Mary's future. Grandma Mary constantly reminded me to count my blessings, being thankful for the right to spend my days as I wish to spend them, because my ancestors didn't have a choice. Their whole lives were spent making white people rich, comfortable, and pleased. At the age of 13, I began taking boxing classes. After several months of training and a couple of fights under my belt. I thought I had the hands of Zab Judah, Bernard Hopkins, or Roy Jones Jr. These were my favorite boxers. Though boxing was my first love, it didn't last long once I grew tired of seeing mothers, fathers, sisters, and brothers of my teammates cheering for them during boxing matches, and hugging while taking family pictures after matches were over. Time after time, I looked around, but no one was ever in my corner supporting me. Respecting my parents as much as I did, made it difficult for me to allow negative thoughts of them being anything less than great parents to last more than half a second. Basketball wasn't my strong suit. Football was fun, but the helmet made me feel like someone could run from the side or back of me without warning, crashing into me as hard as they could. Nope, I didn't like the idea of that. With boxing, I'd be respected in my neighborhood, and get the amount of attention needed from my parents. The neighborhood was easy for me to win over, my parents on the other hand, was not that easy. So, with that said; I washed my hands with boxing. As boxing came to an end, I began smoking weed and getting involved with the wrong crowd, because I wasn't happy at home. Before I go any further, please know that no one is the blame for the decisions that I chose to make except me. I wanted the material things that mom could not afford, and dad didn't care to get me. It wasn't long before selling drugs came into the picture. At the age of 15, myself and a partner of mine named Tru, would go to our spot to skip school, smoke, and talk about all the money we would be rolling around in when we grew up. Our spot was an old 1984 Buick Regal that sat on bricks, but hey, it was our getaway. I sold weed for a guy that was much older than Tru and I. Tru wanted to hustle with me so bad, but he just wasn't disciplined enough. He asked me several times if he could hustle with me, my answer was no every time. If anything went wrong because of Tru's incompetence, the blame would be on me. As time went on, he stayed by my side taking notes on this lifestyle that we saw a career. I eventually started to feel like, maybe you're responsible enough to grind with me and keep the money right. well, as quickly as the thought came it left. I was wrong! He failed every time. This led me to cut him off from the hustle, which made other friends of ours, who were on the outside looking in, put unhealthy things into Tru's head. As weak minded as he was, he bought whatever the haters were selling.

One day I shared with him a dream that I've had more than once where he tried to rob and kill me. We laughed at the silly dream, though I always kept the dream at the front of my thoughts. Grandmother Mary had taught me that.

"Your dreams don't always lie to you". She would say.

2 years later that the dream almost came true. Tru's girlfriend at the time heard a conversation he was having about me with a couple of guys who really didn't care for me. His allegiance was to the so-called friends of ours that couldn't wait to divide and conquer, and he made it easy for them to succeed at doing just that. The time was about 11:30 pm when my cell phone rang, it was Tru saying he needed 4 ½ ounces of cocaine. I wondered to myself why he wanted more dope than I know he can handle, maybe he was finally ready to take his safe serious and put some money into it. I told him as long as he got the money, I'll pay my uncle a visit and bring him what he asked for, and to just give me an hour. After the visit with my uncle, I was riding on the freeway so that I would make it to Tru quicker than I would have had I taken the main roads, plus my chances of running into the police were slim to none. The exit was

coming up soon, I switched lanes preparing to get off the expressway and my phone rang again. Thinking that it was my partner, I answered without checking to see who was calling.

"Yeah, bro, I'll be pulling up to you in about 5 minutes". I said.

"No, this is Tanisha, Sam". The caller said sounding distressed.

"Oh! Hey Nisha, why it sound like you're crying?" I said concerned.

Nisha replied, "Because I have to tell you something".

"OK, go ahead what's wrong?"

"If Tru calls you and try to meet with you for business please don't go Sam. I heard him and two guys saying they were going to rob you, but one of them said he's killing you no matter what."

As Tanisha was talking, I thought to myself about all the times in my life that I've been betrayed by people close to me and asked myself, Why? My mind raced so fast as word after word came out of her mouth, Tru was nothing less than my brother. We shared family, money, clothes, thoughts, and secrets. How did we make it to this point? On one hand, I wanted to have whatever conversation we needed to have to make shit right, but on the other hand I wanted to kill him and the suckas he plotted on me with. I called Tru to tell him something came up so I ain't gonna be able to come through for him. Disappointment after disappointment drove me crazy and my friends and family were becoming unfamiliar to me. So, to feed my emotional hunger, I started messing with different females. I needed to be listened to and have a comrade to believe in me and take on the world with me be by my side at all times. Different women possessed different qualities and strengths that I sought after. Which is why I needed more than one.

When I was 17, one of my girlfriends told me she was with child, and it was good news to my ears, so I quickly manned up. Preparing for my first child- in my mind, everything had to be perfect for her arrival; diapers, clothes, crib, stroller, bottles, baby food, and a father with open arms ready to hold his baby girl. Patrice is the name of my daughter's mom. She was more than my girlfriend; she was my best friend. During her pregnancy, I checked in her everyday making sure she had food and whatever else she needed. I never wanted her to stress, it wasn't healthy for her. June 11, 2002, my baby girl was born. I called Patrice's house to check on her as I did daily. Her sister told me that she went into labor. My thought, why didn't anyone call me? I Called the hospital to let her know I was on the way! Patrice was quiet for a few seconds before speaking.

"Lil Man, don't waste your time coming up here, because my baby daddy is here." Se said in a low tone.

"WHAT" I said in disbelief.

That was the only word I could find to speak. I dropped the phone and ran to room flipping shit overlooking for my gun. My mind went blank and I couldn't remember where I hid it. When I finally found it, I turned around only to find my beautiful mother standing there. She asked what my problem was. I explained what Patrice done to me with water in my eyes that refused to fall down my face. My mom saved my life that day with her words of wisdom

"Do not throw your whole life away for a feeling or pain that's temporary, you're gonna be ok son."

My mom was right, but the pain lasted for months. Yeah, my heart was crushed. That was the straw that broke the camel's back. After another terrible experience I became cold hearted. This bitch that I spent so much time and money on made me look like a fool in front of all my loved ones. I ended a healthy relationship with a beautiful young lady who was faithful to me, her name was Nikki. She's a person I can't get off of my mind, because her feelings got hurt in the situation. I'd give anything to be able to meet her face to face and apologize. It was starting to feel like I was self-destructing. Something on the inside of me made me want to carry a gun on my waist every day and that's just what I did. In and out of jail for shootings, carrying guns, domestic violence, and the manufacturing of drugs was the results of my unhealthy thinking and space I was in. The first shoot-out I had ever been arrested for; I was 17 years old. A friend and I pulled into a store parking lot where we had to meet a guy wanting to buy drugs from us. My homeboy Romeo was driving. He walked into the store to buy some liquor for us because I wasn't old enough. I exited the vehicle to make a sell to the dope fiend we met up with daily. A car with three dudes pulled into the parking lot as well, coming to a quick stop. One of the guys yelled out.

"Come here Lil' Man!"

Only people who really knew me called by my nickname, but they didn't look familiar to me, so I kept walking across the parking lot. Three seconds later, gun shots began to ring out, coming from the same dudes. I returned fire as I ran around to the back of the store and jumped a gate. Making it two blocks over hoping not to run back into them, but they spotted me again driving up the street shooting at me without warning. As I shot back, I noticed the police coming around the corner. There was no way out of this one, we were caught with the barrels of our guns still smoking. An hour later, we were being booked into the precinct. Damn, no more juvenile, it's big boy jail now. Every hearing, court appearance, visiting day, and even my birthday while being in the county jail was spent by myself. I was all I had. Always feeling like a failure, I totally disconnected myself from my family. The streets was my family because they felt my pain and made me feel comfortable about going nowhere fast. My father tried talking to me, but I didn't know how to allow sincere love into my heart, lost is what I was.

When I was 19 years old, I did more time in county jail for a drug charge which was only six months. After my release I finally started to get a grip on my life. It was time for me to really start planning for my future, so first thing first, I obtained a legitimate job even though there was light drug selling on the side. There was a woman, a beautiful woman who came into my life and wanted nothing but the best for me, and to start a life with me. Her name was V. She was older than I was by seven years. She was 26 yrs. old, 5'2, red bone, 160 lbs., but thick in all the right places so she was easy to be with. I was 19, pretending that I knew how to love. One morning after she made me breakfast in bed, V pulled from her purse, eight thousand dollars and put it in my hand. With the money she wanted to put a down payment on a new life together, such as, a family car along with a new place for her two children, myself, and her. Still cold hearted because of my past, I spent the funds she entrusted me with on myself. I don't know how I allowed myself to become so ugly on the inside, but karma is a bitch. March 10, 2005, just two weeks after I selfishly spent V's money, I was due to report to the probation department, and when I arrived there were three detectives. Two men and one woman; they were waiting for the man of the hour, me! In the hands of the lady detective was a warrant with my name on it for Armed Robbery. I never robbed anyone in my life, but of course I knew who committed the crime. Once again, I had to wear another pair of handcuffs. On the freeway as we traveled to the precinct, one detective was cool enough to hold my cell phone to my ear for two calls: my mom and a different woman named Tracey who had been sitting at her breakfast table waiting for me to show up. There wasn't a doubt in my mind; I'm taking this all the way to trial, especially once I discovered that one of two victims clearly stated that I wasn't the guy. Also, in my favor were two sets of videos, the crime scene and police dashboard cam, but neither of the two made it to trial. I'd hoped to prove my innocence, but unfortunately, I was found guilty by a jury not of my peers. After being convicted and sentenced to 15-30 years, it seemed like a long ride to prison but it really wasn't. The ride lasted a few hours. I never had such a short drive that allowed for such a long time to sit and contemplate heavily upon my life; for hours I repeatedly asked myself; How are you going to make it through this? Quarantine is the central prison where everyone goes through to get tested for diseases and health problems. Outside of physical testing, we went through days of orientation preparing us for prison. Looking at the smallest space ever occupied by a human, I had no answer to my question. After 21 days of quarantine, the time came for me to be transferred to a high security level prison where I'd spend the next few years of my life. Prison was very depressing for me, life as I knew it ended in the blink of an eye and made me want to change my situation quick. When friends would come to visit with me, it always turned into a therapy session. After all, who else did I have to talk to? At times when visits couldn't heal my pain, I learned to express my feelings through writing, which is how this very book began to form. My poems started as letters or thoughts I would read to myself, with all that was going on I needed a way or outlet to stay sane. My list of family and friends dwindled before I knew it. I'm extremely thankful for my Mom, Dad, my sisters LaKiesha & Dominique, my best friend that I call my brother Benjamin R., Mr. & Mrs. Walcott, Zippora, and a dear friend of mine LB (Lady Bug).

LB was the most consistent, never missing a beat and always kept open the lines of communication no matter the price or frustration.

Prison made me feel as if I was millions of miles away from what I knew to be home. There was always something going on whether it was violence, gambling, joking, or non-stop movements all around you. The feeling I've always had was, I'm in the projects without a woman in sight. My first three years spent in a Level IV facility (high security level). 3 hours out and 21 hours in. There was action going on every time we came out of our cells. After three years my security level dropped to what's known as a level II (medium security level) 14 hours out, 10 hours in. That was a very different transition. Solitary confinement happens from time to time when you can't avoid trouble. I have stayed up many nights thinking about my life from as far back as I can remember, all the way back to the present day. It's amazing what your brain can do when you finally decide to use it. Fortunately, I was blessed with mail coming on a consistent basis, but one person in particular would write me, and I'd be able to feel her through her words. She was also an inspiration for my writing. Prison was like a small fish tank, and I out grew my environment. The person I have to thank for my mind expanding outside of bricks, bars, yards, and barbed wired fences is my good luck charm "Lady Bug." Her letters and phone conversations always left me with a smile on my face and thinking positively about my future. Genuine is what she has always been to me. Come to think of it, the very first letter I've ever received incarcerated was from her. I'll never forget her contribution to my sanity.

While doing hard time, when no one else was with me; there she was. My incarceration made me feel like a loser, a complete failure so the talk I had with myself is that I will not fold, I will make it out, I will be successful, and I will look in the mirror one day and be proud of the man looking back at me. My heart and soul went into this baby (Book) of mine, so hopefully you enjoy it and you'll grow a new appreciation for life. Life for me isn't over, so Chapter 1 is just a look into my past, right before success starts for me. Please continue to follow me as I head towards the future. As long as I keep waking up every morning and maintain a positive lifestyle, Part two will be in the making. A complete autobiography!

CHAPTER 12

SCATTERED THOUGHTS: "DO YOU"

Do You have morals?

Do you have a constitution?

Do you love your people?

Do you know who you truly are?

Do you strive to be a person of integrity?

Do you educate yourself and those around you?

Do you stand for something?

Do you lead more than you follow?

Do you alter yourself to be around others?

Do you respect another race more than your own?

Do you have order, strength, honesty, unity, goals, truth, vision, or power?

Do you mentally shape your day before it starts?

Do you believe in yourself? Do you help others smile?

Do you dream? Do you build your higher self?

Do you stand up when no one else does?

Do you support negative thoughts?

Does your presence make a positive difference?

Just questions we should ask ourselves sometimes. There's nothing wrong with self-checking.

CHAPTER 13

TENACITY

Ima look y'all in the eyes and smile as if you never said fuck me, even though you did. I stood in front of a judge who asked me if I had anything to say to the court before he read my sentence. At that very moment my soul took over, and I spoke from the core of my essence. But it still made no difference. He just wanted me to speak to him as if he was God. That was the beginning of my fifteen-year fight. The bus ride from county jail to prison was the most depressing ride of my life. The first year of my prison stay, my hands stayed swollen from fighting. Desperately needing an outlet, I began studying law, because I needed to get out of this place. That night before going to sleep. I thought about my ladybug (my girl) whose face I couldn't get out of my mind.

There's something known as an appeal, where mostly every prisoner has the opportunity to bring to the court's attention that their rights were violated. We all hoped to obtain our freedom at the end of this process. In the law books there were always "hidden" laws that contradicts the same law that could help you obtain your freedom. Now, I'm feeling as though I misunderstood what I'd read. This led me to spend hundreds of dollars on prison lawyers who cared more about the chips and pop tarts they would make off of me. They failed at getting themselves out of prison, so they sold hope to desperate individuals. As you're trying and focusing on things more important, you find out that some petty ass thief crept into your cell and stole all your cellmate's stuff (i.e. food, and appliances), and he feels you had something to do with it. Though freedom is on your mind every day, this is a situation you didn't see coming and you must deal with it. This fight won't help you get out of prison, but you better come out on top because it can cost you your life. That night before going to sleep, I gave thanks for my strength, I'm a warrior.

Months later, the Court of Appeals sent their decision back. The letter read, "Your claims have no merit, so this court denies your motion for relief."

Damn, after receiving some news like that I need some energy. Let me call one of my homies.

Ring! Ring! Ring! "Your call has been forward to a voice automated system, please leave your message after the beep."

Alright, he sent me to voicemail, he must be busy, I thought to myself.

I called my sisters Kiesha and Dominique, they always put a smile on my face and say things to put my mind at ease. Fifteen years is a long time to try focusing on something positive while dealing or walking amongst chaos. There's another court I can please after unsuccessfully pleasing the Court of Appeals, which is the Supreme Court. Fuck a jailhouse lawyer, it's mandatory I hustle up on a professional.

Finally, a real lawyer. The first physical meeting we had; I see in his eyes he can care less about my case. His main concern is the check. Long story short, I was unsuccessful with the Supreme Court as well. It felt like the whole justice system had been rigged. Yeah, prison life is hard. I had to become the love I needed to smile, all the prayers I prayed never came through , I had to answer my own prayers, and I wrote letters to myself because nobody knew what I needed to hear. Everything I lacked in my life I had to become, because this fight was getting the best of me and I was all alone. Yeah, I'm an underdog, but you can't find one person to bet against me. Why? Because they know that I'll make it out of hell with the devil's head in my hand. I'm relentless!

CHAPTER 14

UNBROKEN

All the nights I couldn't sleep, you rolled around in beds so big that you couldn't tell anyone was in it. I starved for almost fifteen years while you got fat. I cried till my eyes swelled and you laughed at my pain. While I told you about dreams of living life, everybody lied to me saying "you ain't missing nothing out here." Weeks of solitary confinement played with my sanity, but still my reality was glorified on social media by people who can't relate to my situation. My woman friend lies to me every phone call saying, 'I'm so ready for your release, because I can't take being without you." I been in prison so long my own mother doesn't even know what to say to me anymore, whenever we speak. At one point I prayed, now a days I just sit in silence. This year, I remember my birthday a week after it passed. Damn! What's happening to me? Through all of this and more, I still didn't lose my mind. Friends turned their backs on me because they feel as if they don't need me. And to whoever out there that feel like I'm not important, you don't know me, so let me further introduce myself. Forget my name, where I'm from, and who I know. I'm binary so don't put me in a category, box, or even with a group of individuals that you may see as different from you. I'm all mind, but don't misread me because I'll punish you worse than whoever it is that you worship. I'm smooth as a dairy queen ice cream. I'm righteous enough to hold all the knowledge in the universe and not misuse it. I'm all the love needed to fill voids. I'm intelligent enough to exist in more than one realm. I love every life that walk the face of the planet earth. Yes, I've been through hell and back, but I'm not broken. On my journey, I found something I'll never lose again. Me!

CHAPTER 15

I MET 3 MEN

Wow! Over the years I've met an extraordinary amount of people. Some I'm happy to have met, some were a blessing, but some were heartless, hateful, and I really wouldn't be mad if I never met them. I met a man who was an elderly man that been incarcerated more than twenty years. I've known him for five years of those twenty, and every morning for five years straight he'd wake up bright and early go out to the prison yard. Only to go and stare at the fences that held him captive. For hours he would stare out at the free world, sometimes it seemed as if he never blinked once. Finally, one morning I asked him.

"Mr. Matthews, what's the reason for staring out at the fence every day?"

He said, "One day little brother these gates will fall, and that's the day I'll be free." (He was serving Life)

I also met a man that lived only in his mind, and one day he said to me "Take your life serious and try your damnedest to always make healthy decisions or you'll end up like me.

Imagining yourself living your life." (After serving thirty years he was released)

Lastly, I met a man who always said, "Never stop having faith." One day he screamed "I had enough." He packed every piece of property he owned saying to himself he was ready for release. For a little over six months he kept walking on faith, serving life with the possibility of a parole. After twenty-seven years the parole board finally granted him his freedom. What I learned from these three men along with many others is that, if you're unsatisfied with your today, you must go against the grain to be satisfied with your tomorrow.

CHAPTER 16

DEAR LOVE

When you receive these words, I pray that all is well with you and yours. I'm only writing you so that I can finally rest easy, because right now things are very hard for me because I'm confused, or it may just be me being naïve to the obvious fact. It's a wrap! Which is cool now that it's over. I don't have to feel like a burden anymore, or like I'm holding you back. Lord knows that's a fucked-up feeling. I love you too much to stop you from being a wife to a truly deserving man, and a young mother to a blessed child. The world doesn't revolve around me and what I want, but for the longest time I actually thought it did. Am I mad at you? Yeah, not because you left me, but because we were friends before anything, and you forgot all about that. I'll get over it eventually though. I would drown a glass of water for you, always remember that. I'll always be the one you and your family can count on. Just reach out to me and I'll reach back. Thorough is what I'll remain, anything less wouldn't be Sam. You have nothing to worry about from this point on, this is the last time you will hear from me. I promise my word is bond. The crazy thing about us is that we never seen each other physically, but you were the best girl I ever had, Yeah, that's deep. Since day one, I knew you were too good to be true. Imma street guy, I ain't supposed to believe in fairy tales anyway. But I will admit that I was starting to. Alright! This is my stop; I'll see you if we ever cross paths.

About Dear Love: One day while I was in my cell day dreaming, a letter from love slide under the door with my name on it. Inside love talked about how she thought of me and will never leave my side. After finding out that deception was her only ingredient. I remained the same guy I always been. But, when it comes to her, I guess I never really knew her

CHAPTER 17

TO MY ANCESTORS

Y ou've been through so much. More than any of us currently living could even imagine. We can't relate to the feeling of being kidnapped, taken to a foreign land where you'll never be respected, separated from your loved ones, and sold as livestock. Still through all the abuse, mental and physical stripping, excruciating labor, and murder, you spent your precious time that you were given on this earth as a slave to an immoral people. I will always honor you until I take my last breath, because it's you I have to thank for my tomorrow being better than the one you had. With all the sacrificing you did; you would not believe how the majority of us ended up. We disrespect each other, that ugly word "Nigger" is the new "I love you", and the white man isn't the problem anymore. We are! Families aren't structured or valued, and all intimate conversations are over this object called a cell phone that does things to your body that you wouldn't believe. Places like where I'm from, which is referred to as the "Hood" is flooded by people who never take the time needed to learn about you. They barely care that you even existed. Yes, I know things may sound pretty bad, but don't count us out just yet. There are individuals such as myself along with many others that are conscious and travel against the grain of the common road. More of us are very much needed, because the conscious ones are outnumbered tremendously. My promise to you all is that I won't give up, and I'm willing to die for us if it will create a better tomorrow for those after me just as you have for us.

CHAPTER 18

To my people "The original people"

A ll the way from back in the slavery times all the way up to the present day we've been disrespected, murdered, preyed upon, torn down, and misled. Every day for the past few years I've witnessed on the news station time after time black men being targeted by thugs disguised as policemen. The men they so often target never make it back to their families. Cultural genocide is very real and it's happening before our eyes but for some reason everyone in the black community seems to be focusing on things more important such as drugs, sports, things we can't afford, senseless crimes, unhealthy music, or kissing the ass of the people who can care less about your black ass. Though we're living in a time where knowledge is always at our fingertips, people are acting really fucking stupid. To the individuals in America that see yourselves as "hood, or street guys." Stop dying for nothing and start dying for something. How is it that you are afraid of everything in the world except yourself or those that look like you? To my black people in the entertainment field (i.e. music, movies, sports, theater, etc.). Learn to be that stand-up person when the director says cut instead of only being a strong figure when the director yells action. To the minorities in this country that's a part of the justice system, I understand you took an oath, but where's your integrity? Or did the oath change your identity? I can go on and on, but I feel my point has been made. America is not our land and we'll never feel welcomed here. How long will we constantly witness our brothers and sisters deliberately be disrespected? Stop marching so much, we're becoming predictable, and foreseen. Be as your ancestors would want you to be, try to reflect what your people shed on you in the beginning. A King, Queen, God, Goddess, or just plain Great!

CHAPTER 19

IMAGINE THIS

Imagine a people who were the descendants of Kings,

Queens, Warriors, Scientists, Doctors, Teachers, Mothers, & Fathers of civilization, etc… These people now live in America. Imagine if they knew their worth and who they really were, they loved each other and took care of one another. Powerful is what these descendants would be, and respect is what they would have earned.

Every neighborhood where they reside is clean and drug free, the children loved hearing stories told by elders. The women walked with their heads held high because the men did the duty of a man and made sure she was the standard for every other woman that walks the planet earth. The men were the cream of the crop and was a father to every child that didn't have a father. Men like these were hard to find because of the bravery each other possessed. They smiled and welcomed the face of death whenever one had to give his own life for the protection of benefit of his people. In this case death is viewed as life, because you're all the way free or you're not. Imagine secrets were only kept from those who proved to be irresponsible and couldn't handle a certain degree of knowledge. Plus, not everyone will be a truthful person. Imagine if lust was unable to make people do or say unbelievable things and choosing to hate someone would be considered a weakness. Gossip will be the reason a person gets murdered because gossip breeds nothing except unhealthy energy. Imagine if women didn't answer to bitch, men ears muted the word nigga, and all children wanted greatness for themselves; *Imagine That!*

CHAPTER 20

MIND NOT INCARCERATED

The prison cell that I'm occupying is approximately an 8 X 12 space, which breaks down to 96 square feet. For the time being, this is my living quarters. This is no way for a king to live, but I'm being carried by my supreme self that assist me on pushing forward during strenuous times. Being incarcerated doesn't define me, and it should not define you if you're going through a similar situation. It's absolutely up to you to be built or destroyed during difficult times. My mind is as big as the universe. A person may ask how a space so vast could be compared to a space so small. Well the body possesses infinite power that is within, and once this knowledge is understood we'll stop limiting ourselves.

Prison limits the individual that allow it to. Just as a fish grows based on the size of its tank or bowl. The environment effects the growth potential of any living thing. A domesticated animal. For example, a dog is limited once his/her is locked on a fence that it can't get out of. Understanding this, I realized that it takes more for those who are incarcerated to stay free mentally than it does for the majority of others that are not. This is no excuse for us to overlook our potential, so always keep your thoughts and goals outside of that 96 square feet. Which is symbolic to a grave, most prisoners even call it a tomb, but I consider it a lab (laboratory) where I come up with a formula for every problem that may exist within my universe (my circumstance).

CHAPTER 21

IT'S NOT EASY

D ay after day I have to search out energy to get me going, because the characters that surrounds me are no help. It's up to me. Either I can complain, or I can do something to feel alive in this dead world. Action is what I present to the onlookers. Taking the easy route is difficult, but only because I understand that I have responsibility. I'm the leader in a follower's environment. Without me doing my part, the scale will only lean to one side. There would be no balance. Had I not taken my position, all around me would have been nothing but chaos. Who's going to do it if I don't? Every day is a struggle, and life is constantly a fight. So, to whom this may concern, suit up and prepare to be a champion. *If It's In You!*

CHAPTER 22

DREAMING "THE SUN"

In my dream I walked down the only road in sight. A voice spoke to me

"Samuel, Samuel, Samuel, Samuel! You won't stop until you get an answer to every question you ask before you go to sleep at night."

Not knowing where the voice was coming from, or better yet, who the voice was coming from; I ignored it and told myself to stop trippin. At that very moment some type of vehicle appeared, it looked like a giant titanium marble. When a vertical door opened, the voice said

"get in Samuel, I have something to show you. Something you been wanting to see."

I stepped inside the unique vehicle, the door came down and closed behind me. Everything went silent for maybe 10 seconds, then suddenly a window appeared allowing me to see out of the unbelievably engineered vehicle. There was only one seat inside, and the atmosphere was very comfortable. Without warning it traveled so fast that it was like fast forwarding a movie on the highest speed. I was leaving the earth. For 8.2 seconds the only thing I was able to recognize for sure was a lot of dark space and a bright shining light. The vehicle stopped on a dime never once did I feel any motion. If there had been a cup of coffee sitting on the interior, it wouldn't have moved one bit. The voice spoke to me again.

"Where do you think we are Samuel?"

I replied." This may sound crazy to you and me too, but it looks like we traveled and parked next to the sun."

What blew my mind was how massive the sun actually is, and how the vehicle protected me from the unmeasurable heat along with the brightness. I wasn't hot, plus I was able to look at it without being blinded or have pain in my eyes. The voice spoke once more.

" Yes Samuel, we did just travel to the sun, and the reason for bringing you here is to show you two things to give you the answers to the questions you find yourself asking the most. The first question you frequently ask is, why does it always sound as if someone's calling your name or a voice saying something to you."

The voice asked me to look into the sun and try not to blink. I did, then right at that moment everything went black. A picture of true events appeared. I saw myself standing in a corner inside of a delivery room staring at a woman giving birth to a baby boy. When a nurse showed the woman her child that she just gave birth to, the woman lifted her head. I panicked once I saw who the woman was. I tried with all my might to pull myself out of the vision because I didn't understand the game that the voice was playing with me, but I couldn't stop it. Shortly after, my dad as his young self, walked into the room smiling. The nurse asked if they had a name yet. My mom said "Yes, he's a Jr." In total shock I couldn't believe what my eyes were seeing. This is impossible, I thought over and over in head.

Weeks later, little Samuel was in his crib on a late night. His parents were in their room preparing to go to sleep. I walked over to the baby boy and began talking to him. The baby looked at me as if he really saw my face. He laughed, talking in baby language, and even reached for me at one point. Who can say they had an opportunity to spend time with themselves as an infant? I cut the mobile on for little Samuel, went back to the corner of the room where I sat Indian style until falling asleep. Once waking up, I was in what appeared to be a second-grade classroom. The different color walls in the room were so bright that they made you happy. ABC's & 1, 2, 3's was painted near the ceiling wrapping around the whole upper wall of the classroom.

The teacher introduced herself. "Hi class, my name is Mrs. Robinson and I wanna welcome all of you to my class. How about everyone stand up and introduce themselves to the class."

The first child stood wearing a yellow and white long sleeve shirt, blue jeans, and white gym shoes.

"Hi Mrs. Robinson, my name is Samuel". The kid said

"Hi Samuel, what's your favorite thing about school?"

"Math!"

"Are you good at math?" Asked Mrs. Robinson.

"Yeah, I mean yes. Replied Samuel.

"Well, do you know what 10 plus 5 is?"

Samuel looked down at his little fingers and started counting away. I yelled from the back of the class 15, the answer is 15.

The kid looked up and answered "15."

I clapped loud cheering him on, he looked back into the direction where I stood almost like he heard the loud sound coming from my hands. The voice spoke again.

"I'll show you one more thing and we have to move on."

The next thing shown to me was Samuel as a teenager sitting in his bedroom smoking weed watching a movie titled Belly. In his hand was a vibe magazine. He's reading the very end of it and sees a number for a chat line. He decided to call the number, and the first and only person he connected with will be known to him two years later as Lady Bug, a lifelong friend. The vision ended and the only thing in my sight is the sun, until I looked past the sun at what appeared to be moving balls of light. I asked the voice.

"Are those stars moving in such motions like that?"

The voice replied "NO".

Still watching them as they circled one another, traveling up and down like elevators.

"What are they then, and why are they moving the way that they are?" I asked the voice.

"They're souls, and they're choosing their paths," the voice responded.

Not understanding what he meant about choosing their paths I asked for an understanding. The response was simple but complexed at the same time. He said that the soul possesses infinite energy and can choose to exist on the physical realm whenever it chooses to. "When you witnessed the balls of light going down, they were headed to the earth where at the moment a baby is being born right at that time. The soul will exist within that body until that life is over, with the soul returning to that spot you see where all souls meet. Each soul learns a lesson every life they've lived. Souls are also different ages.

He asked, "Have you ever met or known a child that has made you think they have an old soul?"

"Yes", I replied to the voice.

"You have an old soul too Samuel."

That very moment went black, and another vison started. Flashes from my past life is what I saw, but my face and body was different. I knew it was me because of the connection I felt to the events flashing in front of me. Some things I even remember dreaming about. My home was Africa where I was a part of a tribe, received my gift of a shield and spear (only given to warriors), had a wife, and built a hut for my wife to give birth to my first child. The vision came to a quick stop. The voice spoke:

"I have shown you enough Samuel."

8.2 seconds later I returned to the very road where I heard the voice speak. Every day that I was blessed to see after that dream or should I say experience, was not the same. I know what holds the sun and earth (The solar system). What holds the solar system? (The galaxy). What holds the galaxy? (The universe). My final question to the voice is:

"What holds the universe?"

CHAPTER 23

POEMS FROM AN UNDERDOG

Me and You

Since the day our relationship was born, we've been tight like glue, you appreciate me, and I definitely appreciate you.

The crazy thing is, you saw potential in me before prison, that I didn't see in myself.

You've always been solid to the core of the heart.

These words were manifested from a state of truth, the loyalty and love we have is *True.*

About Poem: This is the first poem that I've ever wrote, it was for a very special person. To me, it was the best poem ever. Don't laugh at me, my poems eventually Gotten better with time.

Family & Friends

Wow!

I never saw this in my future, the day that everything on the outside came to an end. I used to be the man!

Now all I have is 15 years behind bars, only able to call on one friend, how did friends subtract me so easily?

Thirty days ago, I had six women crying, telling me how much they love and need me.

Now I'm in this mirror puzzled, tryna figure out how to get these six blades out of me.

Pain is what I feel, but now is not the time to be weak.

Buckle your seatbelt and tell self, we're going to make it.

Family ain't who they used to be, yeah, I know they're not obligated to me; but how much do they love me?

There has to be a limit, well I wish I knew this before I wasted sincere quality time getting to know y'all.

Because my love was true, free and deep as the ocean, wasn't no potion, just thoroughness mixed with devotion.

About poem: I wrote this poem to my family and friends, whom I spent a lot of time with on a daily basis and who I've known all my life. I thought of these people every day but as for thinking of me it was out sight out of mind. How could you disconnect from me as if you just met me? I felt like maybe the love was never there to begin with.

She's Gone

Boy: Baby, I'm sorry to tell you this, but I might be going away for a long time. We should call it quits and just be friends.

Girl: Don't talk like that, this time won't destroy our future together, I'ma hold you down. We can do it baby.

Boy: It'll hurt like hell if you leave me later as opposed to now.

Girl: Please stop thinking negative, our love is what's gonna keep us strong.

Boy: It's easy for you, because the second you feel the slightest feeling of fed up I'ma be the one stuck swimming in the hurt...

Years later, I feel like back then when I saw the future, you don't even feel bad about leaving me.

I told you to go but you kept saying no.

I needed you to stay but you left anyway, you knew I was a street nigga, because you didn't want it any other way.

Were you in love with me or the life I lived?

You were a part of my reality; I was a part of your fantasy.

Deep-down I knew you would abandon me.

I tried not to be, but you damaged me.

Prison for me is hell!

Still in all my head stay high because thorough guys always prevail.

About Poem: Anybody who's incarcerated can relate to this type of conversation.

In Love Alone

I'm in love alone, feeling like love is strong even though love is gone.

But that's what I get for not keeping my love at home.

Can't believe I tried to get love from a stone.

Now a days the only real conversations is over the phone.

Muthafuckas ain't no different than a drone.

If I was a dog, you still couldn't be my bone.

Men think love is a beautiful chick in a thong, Women think love is a rich man that owns a hundred homes. Kids think love is every influence that exist outside their home.

Love ain't easy, love is hard, and you'll never find it in somebody else's backyard.

I'm in love alone, feeling like love is strong even though love is gone.

That's what I get for not keeping my love at home.

I see I'm not the only one tryna get love from a stone.

About poem: People, in my opinion have forgot what love is. Love is not material things, lust, or negative influence. Love is deep, unconditional, and shown more than told. The more love I showed, the more people hurt me; So, I must be in love alone.

Forgive Me

How can you hate me when I made me?

Nigga, you ain't pray for me, mold me, or shape me, all you ever been was fake to me.

Talk in bout we a team, I read between the lines.

All you wanna do is play wit me, if you had one wish would you use it to erase me?

You might as well, it's better than living life in hell.

So called family ain't nothing but a body, demonstrating nothing more than a shell.

Yeah, I feel like that,

And if I saw somebody kill you, I won't tell.

Damn, I'm wrong for dat, but you ain't wrong for all dem

wounds on my back.

I still won't smile when yo lifeline go flat.

Might donate a tear; Get high; then fix my hat, life goes on.

I used to wonder why but now I know!

The weak only hate the strong.

About poem: I was having a bad day when these words were produced, but it's the true feelings of a person who's disliked by people most close to them for being who they are, or true to themselves.

Mental Strength

Standing in a room fighting with four walls, I punch hard at them all, but they just won't fall.

I'm thinking bout giving up, with some voices in my head telling me to go head.

My choice was to be strong, so I blocked them out instead.

Thinking about my life and how I'm ready for it to change.

Mad at everybody, but me, when I'm the one to blame.

Why can't anybody else feel my pain?

I bet you can't imagine what it takes to stay sane.

Running with the wolves, wrestling with bulls.

Freedom is something I can't push so I'm looking for a pull.

Been chewing on knowledge for years and I still ain't full.

I'ma winner nigga, so don't ever expect me to lose.

These bricks keep talking, but I'ma swing until they bruise.

The fight getting hard, but I refuse to stop.

Why y'all bricked keep laughing?

Because the door not locked.

About Poem: This poem describes a battle that I went through more than once during my incarceration. As you can see, I made it out that "room" every time. I had to be born a warrior. I am he that shines day and night.

What My Life's Like

My life is like, kickin it with the most loyal person I've ever met, we're talking about things we wanna experience in life, But I have an out date and he don't.

My life is like, running into your old friend you ain't seen in years in prison. He looks the same, but his sexual preference changed.

My life is like, telling the only friend I have left on the outside, that I won't be home when she wants me there, and now waiting on the inevitable which is her leaving.

My life is like, stabbing a guy over some ramen noodles, he

refuses to pay you, because that's what prison guys do.

My life is like, working a job that pays only $20 a month.

My life is like, my father is doing life in prison.

My life is like, losing family members to the sky, never getting a chance to say goodbye.

My life is like, fucking paper bitches not being able to reproduce, so frustrated that I'm filling my liver with spud juice.

My life is like, looking in a mirror with tears in my eyes, because I see a stranger and can't remember the day we met.

My life is like, being proud of nothing cause all I have is regrets.

My life is like, being 30 years old and unable to "one" life accomplishment except my health.

My life is like, hoping to succeed by writing poems to sell while I'm sitting in a cell.

About poem: Life is what you make it, and at the time this poem was produced I didn't like what I made. Everything in life is a decision and I have to start making the right ones.

Wake Up

I feel the pain coming through my window.

As I ride through my city all I see is windows that never got the chance to feel.

How being somebody's wife feels, I feel bad for the kids.

I wanna save them and go, how much cash would it take?

I wish I had to blow, everybody got it hard.

The streets so cold you need more than a coat; you need a heart fresh out the freezer.

The only time my girl act right is when I treat her like she's another nigga skeezer, What a damn shame.

On top of that she wanna have my kids, baby girl some people just not fit to be parents. Especially when she'll leave her baby for some dude who got a car she can't pronounce.

The things of this western world got my people gone, it took them by storm, And I don't know if they'll ever wake up and get themselves back.

To be real, sometimes my smile is the representation of hope.

I guess I'ma have to be our savior cause Jesus taking too long,

Not that I was waiting anyway, But I can't say the same for the rest of my family.

Since the day my people arrived on the land known as America, they've been taught to Wait, Depend, and Expect.

Well lean on me now, your savior in the flesh continue to pray but learn to believe in yourself.

About poem: My aim was to give eyes to the blind and up lift those that are low.

Happy Anniversary

Let this day be a reminder of the day you met your soulmate!

The feeling you felt, the thoughts you thought.

Before the happily ever after, before the children, before the first time you said you love each other.

God had a plan for you, a long life and a beautiful partner to live with.

Reflect on the times you had, the good and the bad, be thankful for everything that comes with life, the present and the past.

Love is something that is to be cherished and celebrated, so look at each other and share a laugh, then say to your partner, "I'm glad you're you, My better half".

Poem dedicated to my favorite couple Mr. & Mrs. Walcott

Necessary Behavior

Day after day you open the same wound.

Got my game face on, but it feels like everybody pointing at me in the room.

Why you so paranoid?

Cause I been through some shit, and feeling like a target,

ain't the shit.

Everybody got two faces, the one they show you and the one they don't.

So, I always strike first.

My loved one's bruised me, so trust ain't in me, don't talk that trust shit to me, prison is a hungry world and weak dudes is the food.

Always ready is what you gotta be, no matter if you in the mood. You call it paranoid; I call it stayin' alive.

Either you're gonna make it or you're not, I was determined to.

If you're reading this, I hope this is nothing you ever have to go through.

About poem: All it takes is one mistake, and that one mistake can do some major damage in your life. People say that I'm too serious, paranoid, and super cautious. I say they're not serious or cautious enough.

What Eye See

I'm on the inside looking out.

You're on the outside looking in.

When you're free the right wind can make you grin.

In this world your enemy is your friend, the truth is a lie. What's real about life insurance? Somebody can't wait until you die.

The sun still shines, even though it's unappreciated.

The moon still glows, even though her existence is underrated.

Show a reformed street nigga a bag, he gone be ready to shake it.

Love is a war tactic, the only time you should grab at it, is when it's in a waste basket.

True love always gets thrown away.

Our ancestors suffered and died every day, and nobody have enough decency to say thanks, but if we were repaid for how they were treated, yo fake ass would be the first one at the bank.

I'm on the inside looking out.

You're on the outside looking in.

We're still not free, being killed because we own this beautiful skin.

About poem: I consider myself to be a conscious individual, but everybody sees the world through their eyes only. So, every now and then I like to snap my fingers in front of my people's face to get their attention.

Real Don't Exist

How it feels to be real?

I'm the only one that know cause all these limitations treat me like I'm fake still.

I look out for people and don't gossip, because I don't, everybody think I got a problem.

Boi you got 15 years cause you didn't rat?

Boi you crazy as hell fa dat.

My girl still mad I didn't rat, I look at her in disbelief, to know that she can really love somebody that's weak, with no bone in his back.

If I would've ratted my name woulda been all in the streets.

Everybody chasin me like an addict, but since I didn't; My name is hard for them to say, kinda like it hurt.

They quit me cold turkey, this the thanks I get for being Real?

Now I know how sacrificing yourself for nothing feels.

Man, next mothafucka that tell me he real go get killed.

Ain't got no gun but I got this ten-inch steel.

Millions of dollars don't make you real.

Running with a squad don't make you real, and just cause you the only one that know your gay don't make u real.

Swag don't make you real either boi.

What you're built like on the inside?

Tell me what you think I don't wanna know.

For a million dollars you will do some strange thangs, And that ain't no real change, but it's enough for you.

Real niggaz to intentionally allow yourself to be played. You should let me pay you to finish my prison time.

Now you looking at me like I'm outta my mind.

How it feel to be real?

Man, I can't say that word anymore, it's time for me to go.

About poem: I was in love with the streets when I was in them. The streets didn't feel the same about me. To the "REAL", they never even thought of me. I'm thankful that I have a way out of this hole I dug for myself. The most important person in your life have to be you.

I Stand Alone

I'm in a land filled with over a thousand strong, but yet I stand alone.

My mind is strong, my voice has a unique tone, my skin is dark, and every word I speak comes from my heart.

I am the original man. I stand for something, so don't expect me to fall for anything.

Yo whole conversation is rims and cane, so we don't talk much, I'd rather stand alone.

Can't tell you shit about running them streets and countin' dem grams, why don't you love yo woman like you love ya mans? And she still holds you down.

Damn I love my people, but the majority of them hate themselves, So I love 'em from a distance, fuck you and yo opinion, you dirt and I'm rinsing.

Christ walked to his death alone, because nobody else is that strong.

Why did my people become slaves? Because nobody else was as strong.

We need to wake up before the people who can teach us be gone, stop playin' with life and understand that it ain't no rap song, Ain't nothing wrong with standing alone.

Cause two kings can't share one throne.

Fakin & shakin, smiling & pounding, maybe he can't, But I can see yo insides frowning.

He robbed you on the street. Now y'all at the microwave sharing something to eat?

I refuse to be a part of this madness, Half of these niggaz mentally already in a casket, leave me alone and let me be, cause when I'm alone that's when I'm Free.

About Poem: After taking a thorough look at everything that was going on around me, I wanted to deliver myself from an unbelievable environment that seemed to bother only me. One day while in deep thought, the poem standalone came about. Out of thousands of people no one was living, everyone's just existing. I had to express myself, and writing was the only way to do it.

Responsibility

I am intelligent, I am unique.

I understand those that don't understand themselves.

I have a responsibility.

No, I'm not perfect, I'm not attractive because I'm not tryna be, I have a responsibility.

Yes, I have many flaws, I'm not the richest or coolest guy in the world, But I'm me quite naturally.

I have no fony personality, and I love my individuality.

How could you hate me when I'm you?

How could I hate you when you're me?

If these words seem crazy, you ain't looked in the mirror lately, killing your brother cause his flag a certain color, you hate gays but yo man's undercover, Get real!

We have children to raise, families to support, women to save, Communities to clean up, elders to help, a culture to restore, A legacy to leave, ancestors to please, devils to dodge, a crisis to stop, and a people to get back.

We have a responsibility, so take your position.

About poem: To the poem points the finger at, it's time to do your duty. We've been distracted for too long. Wake up and get to work and start behaving as men, and not clowns.

Dear Momma

Dear momma, I cry with no tears in my eyes, My favorite movie is any one telling a story about an underdog, Reggae is my favorite music, My favorite food is stew chicken & rice, These are some things you don't know about me. ·

Dear momma, I've been in prison ten years now, but it's been eleven since I've seen you, do you miss me? You would be proud of the man I groomed myself to be, there's no man in your life more thorough than me, you soon will see, and believe it or not, you mean the world to me. You just don't know how to love me, but I ain't mad at cha.

Dear momma, A lot of times I cut my T.V. off to stare at the black screen, I create my own visions, your son is mentally strong, every day I dedicate 20 minutes to you. If I told you you're worth, you probably wouldn't believe it, but I know it; And Ima keep it, I'm the only living man you can count on that'll never let you down, After reading this, the only feeling you should have is, I wanna see my son now. It breaks my heart knowing I haven't seen you in a while, how did you go so long without seeing yo child?

Dear momma, Prison wasn't my choice, it just happened, for some reason I'm not feelin' yo love. Tell me what happened, I love you with all my heart, please don't let the distance tear us apart.

About poem: Please know my mom and I have a beautiful relationship, it's just that she's not a lovey dovey type of person. During my incarceration she never once came to visit me, but my love and respect for her still remains as if she was in the visiting room every week non-stop. This poem was me having a conversation with her in my mind, and expressing myself. I love you momma and I hope you see the love that's in my heart for you.

Power U

Power U is the truth, it makes itself small enough for a man to enjoy pleasure yet will open up wide enough for a life to come through.

God's greatest secret called "creation" reveals itself deep down in every woman's tunnel. Many of us take women for granted, but we'll cherish something material that may cost hundreds of thousands of dollars without realizing that we have in our life the most expensive gift known to man.

But we got her for free, treating her like she grows where we can just pick her from a tree.

She's the bridge we cross before our existence is known to

the rest of the world.

Power U is the healthiest, and safest place on earth.

All the elements of life are there, working without one ingredient to get the process going (the seed from healthy man).

This beginning is called the genesis.

A True Woman

Agape love is all you've ever shown me, Kiki is your hood rat name but that's my homie.

It's hard to believe we're now over thirty.

Look at my pictures and say you still want me.

Anonymous you my wife, yeah that look good on me, Love is all I got right now, Cause I let these white folks out smart me.

Officially man and woman were meant to be.

Trinidadian queen made just for me.

Too good to be true, that's how I feel sometimes.

About poem: Simply put, the woman who inspired this poem held a special place in my heart. Not only did she show me love, she showed me Agape love. Study your bible to understand Agape love.

The Perfect Day

I woke up feeling this day.

Ate a great meal with zero complaints.

During mail time I received four letters, one was from my sister dropping me a line, just to say hey.

My day went so good, I even called my mom hoping to make her day.

Nobody got hurt, so negativity please stay away.

The birds aren't running from people, they're hoping they want to play.

The sun is shining with just the right temperature.

An old man was laughing so hard he had to catch his dentures.

The female officer looked at me and winked, no lust came to my mind.

Only motivation on getting back to the streets.

Got an e-mail from my girlfriend saying the only man she wants is me.

After that, I had a long daydream about freedom. The many things I wanna do in life.

I wish I could live in my thoughts, But I can't.

The outcome of everything is decisions.

For once my whole day was perfect, but all the things I did to come to prison, *Was it worth it?*

About Poem: Things can always be worse than what they are, it's all on your perception. Negativity isn't hard to find, so I can focus on the positive. I had to come to prison and lose everything just to start paying real attention to my life. *I'm woke now!*

<u>Dog Tags</u>

Two dog tags on the same chain, one is for me, the other is your name.

For as long as we're in love, I pray things stay the same.

We'll never be perfect, but our love is not in vain.

At times I take the wrong turn, because all I know to look for is pain.

You're the last woman to have my trust, cause all they wanna play is games.

But many men are not really leading, so I guess we're the blame.

I love you enough to share my chain, which is my life, hopefully you want me the same.

About poem: I was on the verge of losing someone I was emotionally tied to. For many years I called her Lady bug, so that's what I'll say her name is. There were times during my incarceration when nobody would answer their phone for me when I was in need. Lady Bug always took care of me, she's the love of my life. If it wasn't for prison we'd be married. Then again, I don't know because she always says to me "The world don't revolve around you Samuel."

Take Care of Business

I don't like to let certain people get close to me, why do you wanna know me?

We don't have anything in common, the difference between us is that I'm not common.

There's a reason why God is worthy of separation.

I want my family to see me as a blessing, you pray for unimportant things and see them as a blessing.

I can't allow my ancestors sacrifice to be in vain, I love and respect those that came before me and never speak their name in vain.

My focus is my future and becoming a great black man.

Don't overlook your greatness.

Love yourself black man.

Put the same energy into your family as you do your friends.

Start looking for a wife and get rid of those women you call friend.

Most people don't wanna know you, they wanna know your

business.

I have a limited amount of time to save my people.

Now that's taking care of business.

About poem: As men I feel we have a super responsibility to be who we were put on earth to be, but how many of us men do our part? I chose to lead by example. When I take a look behind me, I'm hoping to see many men.

Ms. Anonymous

You are the best thing that will ever happen to me.

I have your heart, but that's because you gave it to me.

If you weren't mine whose would you be?

Scratch that question, because we'd have to start life over to see.

You are for me and I am for you, I want five kids, but you only want two.

No one else means the world to me, so two will have to do.

You may need me, but I really need you, what else do you want from me except the truth?

You're easy to be with and hard to be without.

Forget what people say, we're for life the fire that not even water can put out.

About poem: My life partner has yet to show her face, but I think about her every day. These words are for you.

Just Speaking the Truth

All the shit I been through, boi do it look like I'm playing?

I've had many hard days, your advice didn't work so I been stopped prayin, and I don't give a fuck about yo opinion.

You looking at a nigga who ain't never felt the feeling of winning.

I'm on a mission tryna get it.

Get what? Anything except a chain-rang-and a bad bitch that's go bring me fame.

You can keep all that, cause ain't nothing real attached to no bullshit like that.

I need a wife with potential to raise intelligent kids and understand that I'm knowledge and she the wiz (wisdom).

I yearn to know my ancestors beginning.

Wish I could have a vision of the first day the earth started spinning.

Why is this important? Because it's looking like the world is coming to its ending, And I'm determined to live before it do.

I have an excuse, I been in prison for the past eleven years,

How about you?

Hold on, I'm feeling like Michael Brown.

My hands up don't shoot, I understand you mad but I'm just speaking the truth.

And hell naw I don't wanna rap, Ain't shit cute about hallucinating in a booth.

What's the true identity of you?

I bet you wish you knew, but it ain't yo fault.

Blame it on the lack of education giving to our youth.

Once again, don't shoot!

I'm just speaking the truth.

About poem: It speaks for itself.

My Look is Original

My beard is the beauty of a man.

Its nappy but it was all part of the plan.

My skin resembles dirt, yours resembles sand.

Don't smile just yet because sand is bland.

You smiled anyway cause you don't understand what I'm saying.

Nothing grows from sand.

Everything grows from dirt.

So, remember the next time you make jokes, I need you to know they won't hurt.

About poem: Just a reminder to anyone dealing with ethnic issues, to love yourself and who you came from. Beauty is only in this original form, just as truth is one.

Without You

Without you is a new feeling that I hate feeling.

Why do I dislike myself so much?

All you wanted was for me to tell you how I feel.

The energy that I gave off was that a real man must remain tough, basically I wasn't giving enough.

I miss you telling me how your day went and you asking about mine.

Your smile always gave life to mine.

For eleven years straight you were all about me helping me do my time.

You deserve to be a mother, you deserve to be a wife, you deserve a man that never had prison be a part of his life.

Once he's been with you, he's not gonna be able to be without you, trust me.

I'm at the bottom of my emotions right now.

It's dark down here, so dark I can see my thoughts.

You were my light; it looks like my Lady Bug finally took flight.

Leave some good luck with me, and whenever I talk to you in your thoughts, don't ignore me.

About poem: Self-explanatory.

R.I.P

R.I.P To my loved ones, and those that I don't know, but still pay my respects to.

I'm sorry for being absent when you departed from us.

Not being able to be there to say goodbye to you really hurt me.

Your energy returned back to the source in which it came therefore, I don't have to worry about you.

The way some of you returned to the essence wasn't a smooth transition, it was violent, uncalled for, and plain hateful.

But there's a reason for everything. I have memories of you so you will never be forgotten, your presence will be felt as if you whispered in my ear and said, "Make sure they feel me."

You can always count on me for that.

Everyone you left behind loves you and wonder if they'll ever see you again.

We all want to know what it's like on the other side.

You know the things we don't about the afterlife, so you're quite a few steps closer to being "All Knowing."

We love you and will one day join you once the arms on the clock moves no more.

Rest and live in peace.

She Came and Left on Her Birthday
12/18/13

Hey little one, I woke up with you on my mind as I often do.

I wish, I was able to send God a card and letter so he can read them to you for me.

We miss you so much.

Little ladybug, you departed from us oh so soon, which is the reason you and I never had the chance to meet one another.

It's known that you're not my daughter, but I love you no different than my own.
You are so special that God wanted you more than we

needed you, so you were unable to stay with us.

Don't worry about her though, I make her smile every chance I get, even though I drive her crazy.

Your physical presence blessed us almost three full hours and it was just you and your mom.

You brought her happiness that nobody else could bring her.

Thank you for your presence.

You and my mom share the same day that God allowed life to share you guys with us, so you're forever in my heart.

Your name without a doubt on my list of favorite people.

Every year on your birthday I make it about you, spending it with you on my mind.

Live good on the other side little ladybug, we love you.

Rest and Live In Peace Y'all

Carleen Grooms
Kalvin Profit (K-9)
Mary Wilson
Anthony Washington (Doe Boy)
James Carden (J-9)
DeMarco Profit (Marco)
Mariah Grooms
Crishana King (Crissy)
Gary Profit
Patrick Houze (Pat)
Brint Terrell
Montez Profit (My-G)
Michell Profit (Renee')
Anna Mae London
Clerance Irving
Harris Shuler
Anisa Walcott
Kyreisha Ward (Kyree)
All the brothers & sisters slain by law enforcement
Our Ancestors
Gladas Grooms
Elizibeth King Francis
Carolin Coats
Judy
Sean Strickland
Rahsaan Greir
Margrett
Eric

Quotes That Inspired Me

- "Never trust a person that talks more than they do anything else."

- "Everything in life is a decision." -Samuel Profit

- "Where there is no vision, the people perish." -Proverbs 29:18

- "Plans fail for lack of counsel, but with many advisers they succeed." -Proverbs 15:22

- "The only tired I was, was tired of giving in." -Rosa Parks

- "Never let a man take your thoughts." -Samuel Profit

- "A man is literally what he thinks, his character being the complete sum of all of his thoughts." - James Allen

- "He that walks with wise men shall be wise." -Proverbs 13:20

- "Why pursue your dreams at 5 mph when can go 65." -Steven K. Scott

- "You can't beat an enemy that you don't understand." -Steve K. Scott

- "We should not look back, unless it is to derive useful lessons from past errors." -George

Washington

- "Most people think they know the answer. I am willing to admit, I don't even know what the question is." -Arsenio Hall

- "A person completely wrapped up in himself makes a very small package." -Denzel Washington

- "Formal education makes you a living. Self-education makes you a fortune." -King Yatta

<u>The Difference between a Boy and a Man</u>

Boys are students ** Men are teachers

Boys are consumers ** Men are producers

Boys play with toys ** Men work with tools

Boys break things ** Men make things

Boys ask questions ** Men give answers

Boys are disruptive ** Men bring order

Boys run in gangs ** Men organize teams

Boys shack up ** Men get married

Boys make babies ** Men raise children

Boys won't raise his own ** A man will raise his and somebody else's!!!!

Boys invent excuse for failure ** Men produce strategies for success

Boys look for somebody to take care of them ** Men look for somebody to take care of!!

Boys are present- centered ** Men are time balanced, having a knowledge of the past and understanding of the present and a vision for the future!!!

Boys seek popularity ** Men demand respect

Boys are up on the latest ** Men are down with the greatest

Coming Soon...

Self-Made In The Dark Vol. 2

Self-Made In The Dark Vol. 3

Angel Cupcakes

Hidden Consciousness

Author Contact Information:

Email: samuelprofit2020@icloud.com
Phone: (248) 429-7974
Facebook: Samuel Profit